The Thinking Tree

LIFE SKILLS

ACTIVITY BOOK

For Active & Creative Kids
STEP BY STEP GUIDE

WRITTEN BY MELISSA DOUGHERTY AND SARAH JANISSE BROWN

Illustrated by Anna Kidalova

The Thinking Tree LLC

FUNSCHOOLING.COM

How to Use This Book:

This book is designed to teach you many valuable life skills. Search for the information about each skill but make sure that you also practice what you've learned!

Learning Tools Required to Complete this Course:
- Pencil and colored pencils
- The Internet to search for videos or articles OR books on each of the topics
- Creativity!

Additional Materials You Will Need to Practice Your Skills:
- A house plant
- Your bed
- A smart phone or computer to access applications like Zoom, Google Meet, etc.
- A crochet hook and yarn
- Sewing supplies
- Telephone
- Thank you cards, envelopes and stamps
- Cleaning supplies
- Tea bags, stove/microwave to heat water
- Tape measure
- Iron and clothing
- Dictionary and Thesaurus
- Lightbulb
- A tie
- A vehicle and a gas station
- Map of your city
- Knives
- Wrapping paper, scissors, tape
- Poster board, markers

Table of Contents

Skill #1 –
Basic First Aid

Draw a picture of each book you will use to learn more about this topic:

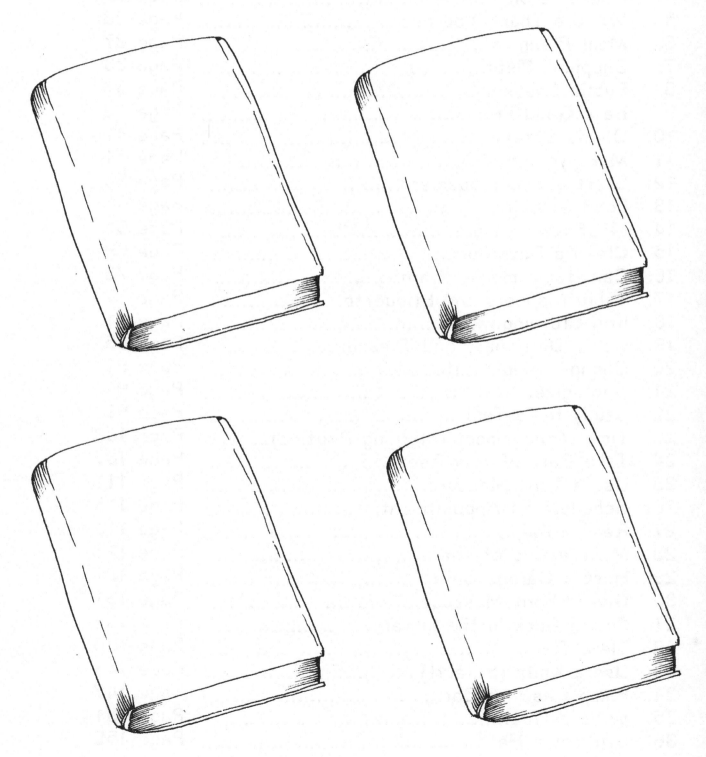

Take notes from your books or videos about how to handle the following situations:

Cut or scrape:

Bloody nose:

First degree burn:

Bruise or Bump:

Allergic reaction:

Concussion:

Watch a video or read about **WHEN** and **HOW** to call 9-1-1

List some situations you learned about in which you should call for help:

1.

2.

3.

4.

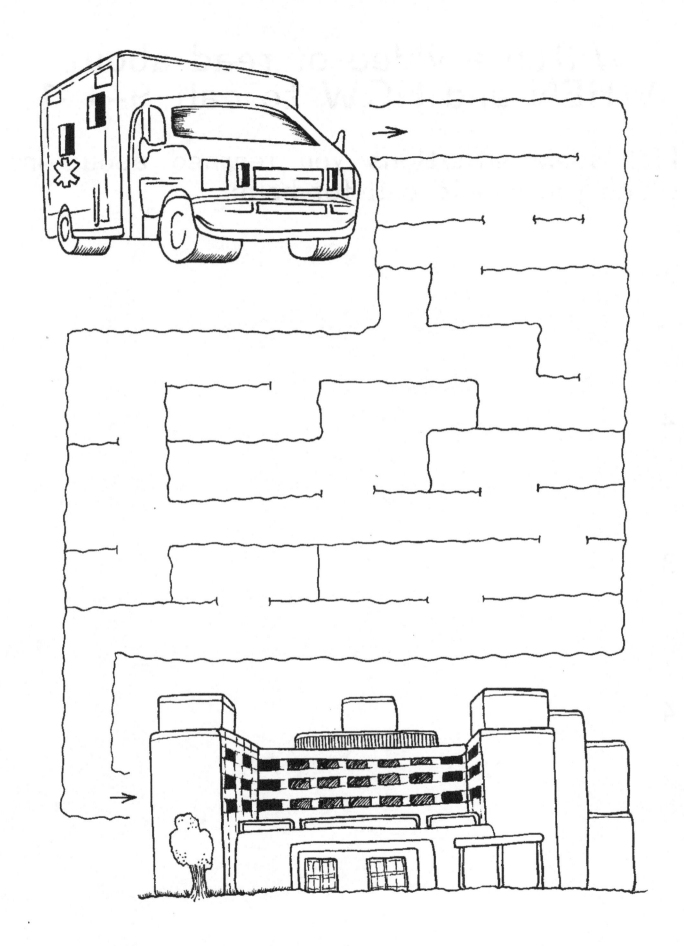

Did you come across any new words while you were learning about types of emergencies?

Write the definitions of **5** new words below:

1.

2.

3.

4.

5.

6

Skill #2 –
How to Do Laundry

Go through your closet and read the tags on your clothing. Circle the names of fabrics below that you have in your wardrobe. If your parents give you permission, look at their clothing too!

Acetate

Cotton

Polyester

Linen

Spandex

Wool

Silk

Research each of these different types of
fabrics and how to care for them:

COTTON

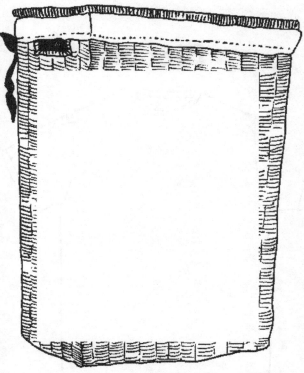

SILK

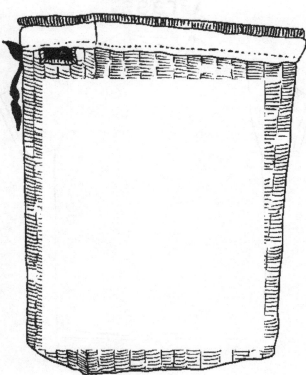

POLYESTER

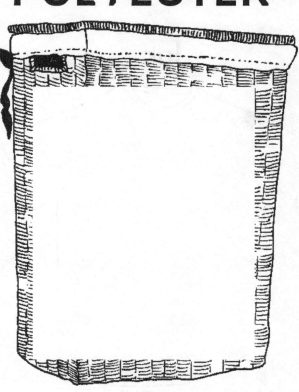

WOOL

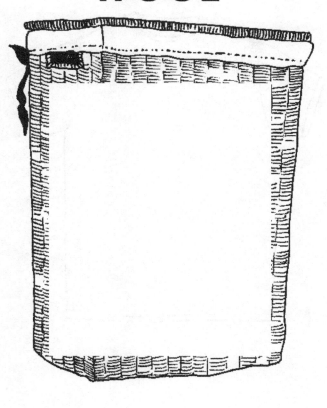

How do you get rid of each of these types of stains? Write your answers.

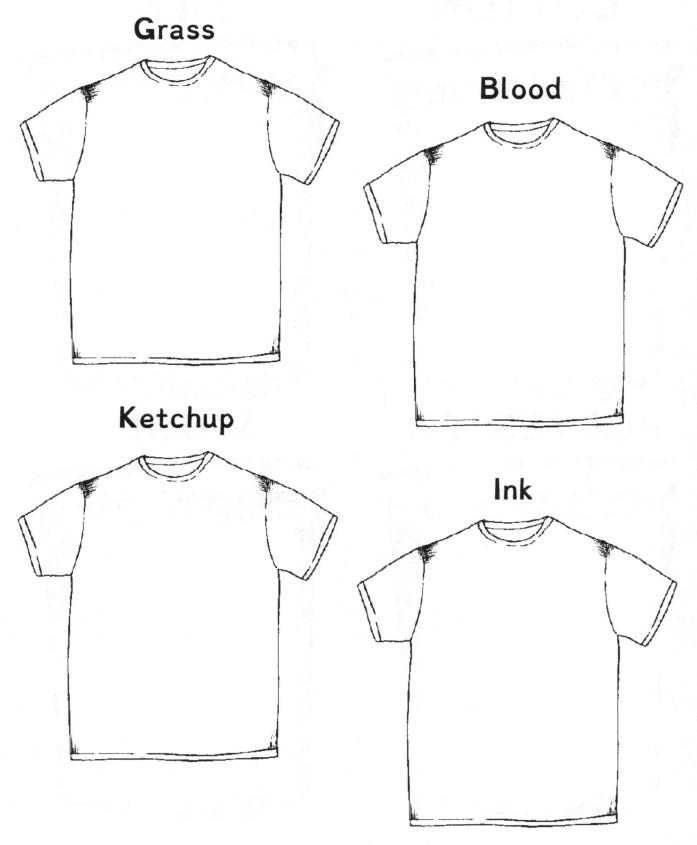

Grass

Blood

Ketchup

Ink

How do you get rid of each of these types of stains? Write your answers.

Sweat

Chocolate

Bubble Gum

Mud

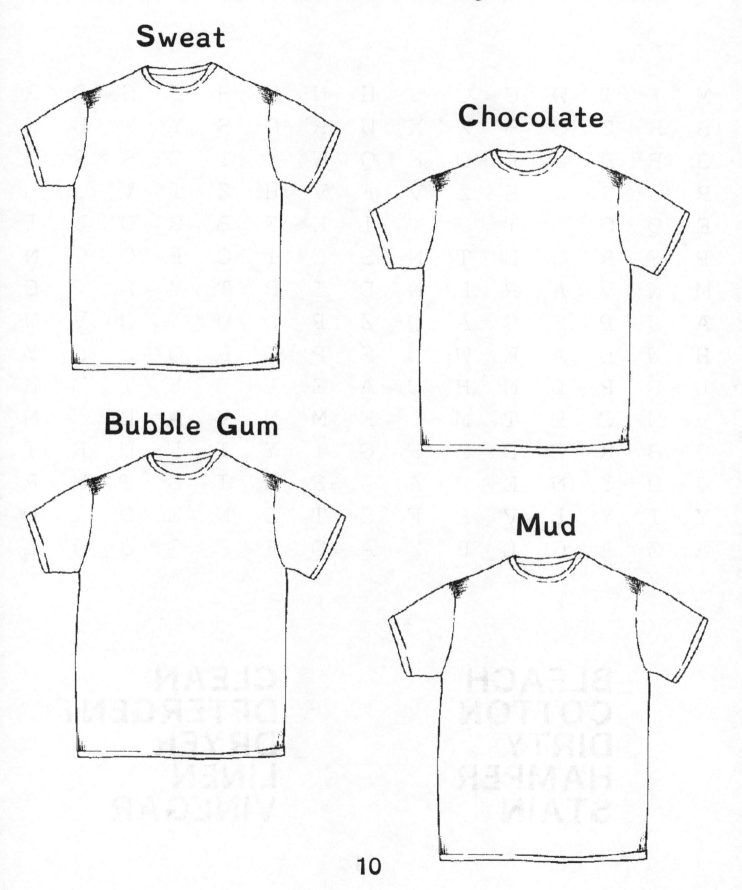

LAUNDRY WORD SEARCH

```
M  I  T  W  U  C  S  H  N  U  H  T  S  D  R
S  R  Z  G  B  X  X  U  R  O  S  Y  W  D  K
S  B  B  J  D  D  K  Q  W  X  T  C  R  R  W
R  J  R  J  E  Z  V  F  V  H  Z  T  V  O  L
E  Q  C  D  T  P  T  I  E  Z  B  R  O  U  I
P  F  R  C  E  T  N  S  C  I  C  F  O  C  N
M  N  V  A  R  E  N  D  I  R  T  Y  E  P  E
A  J  P  F  G  A  Q  Z  P  D  U  I  Q  V  N
H  W  B  A  E  W  D  E  P  D  R  Q  S  S  Y
L  D  R  L  N  H  C  A  E  L  B  Y  T  M  H
V  U  C  E  T  M  S  E  M  N  V  A  E  I  M
J  B  K  C  D  Z  F  G  I  Y  I  F  U  R  I
J  U  Y  N  E  P  A  A  S  N  I  G  F  N  R
Y  I  Y  L  V  E  F  S  T  S  N  E  O  C  D
A  Z  A  C  L  B  Z  A  O  F  E  Q  J  J  L
```

BLEACH   **CLEAN**
COTTON   **DETERGENT**
DIRTY   **DRYER**
HAMPER   **LINEN**
STAIN   **VINEGAR**

11

Which water temperature should you use in each of these situations?

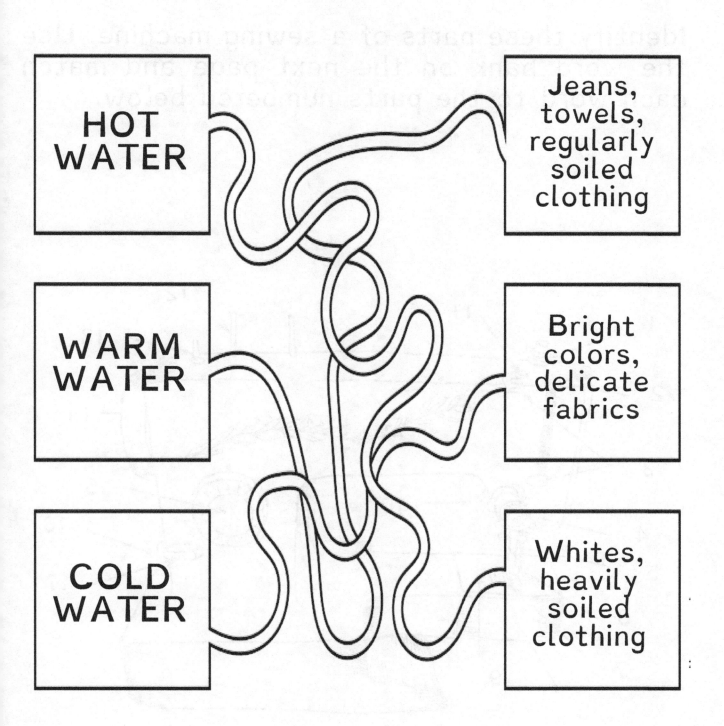

HOT WATER

WARM WATER

COLD WATER

Jeans, towels, regularly soiled clothing

Bright colors, delicate fabrics

Whites, heavily soiled clothing

Skill #3 –
Sewing

Identify these parts of a sewing machine. Use the word bank on the next page and match each word to the parts numbered below.

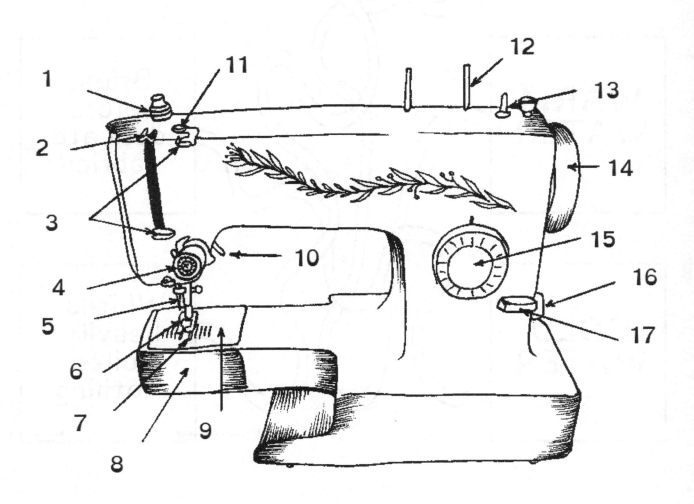

WORD BANK

- Spool Pins
- Pressure Regulator
- Thread Guides
- Feed Dogs
- Throat Plate
- Reverse Stitch Lever
- Stitch Length Dial
- Bobbin Winder Tension Disc
- Presser Foot Lever
- Shuttle Cover (Bobbin Housing)

- Hand Wheel
- Needle
- Bobbin Winder
- Presser Foot
- Stitch Selector
- Take-Up Lever
- Tension Control

1. _____
2. _____
3. _____
4. _____
5. _____
6. _____
7. _____
8. _____
9. _____
10. _____
11. _____
12. _____
13. _____
14. _____
15. _____
16. _____
17. _____

Learn the meanings of all these words.
Write a definition or draw a picture to help
you remember what they mean.

Seam

Right Side

Wrong Side

Back Stitch

Lock

Straight stitch

15

Watch an instructional video about how to sew. Find a project for beginners. If you have access to a sewing machine, choose a video that will instruct in that. If you don't, choose something about hand sewing projects.

Then, choose a sewing project to practice your new skills! Draw a picture below of what you made.

Color the Buttons

Learn to sew on BUTTONS

Here's a project that will help you practice your new skills. Watch a video or read about how to sew a button hole and button. Then, you can make a superhero cape!

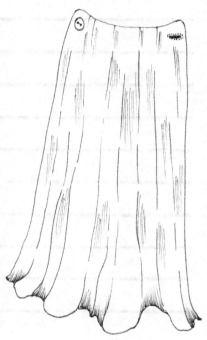

STEPS

1. Measure the width of your shoulders to determine how wide your cape should be.

2. Measure the length from the top of your back to your knees to determine the length of your cape.

3. Cut your fabric **1** inch wider and longer than your measurements to leave room for sewing a hem.

4. Sew a hem around the entire edge of your fabric.

5. In the top corners of your fabric, create a button hole on one side, and sew a button onto the other side.

6. If you want to personalize your cape, you can cut out designs and sew them onto your cape as well.

Skill #4 –
How to Converse on the Telephone

Watch a video and write down some tips you learn about how to use good manners on the phone.

_____

_____

_____

_____

_____

_____

_____

_____

_____

_____

                        _____

                        _____

                        _____

                        _____

                        _____

                        _____

                        _____

                        _____

                        _____

Practice your phone skills by making these phone calls. Put a check mark next to each one once you've completed it.

☐ 1. Call a pizza place and order pizza for lunch. Make sure your mom is willing to pay for it first! Write down below what size of pizza you'll order and what toppings you'll want. Write down the price they give you, so you can tell your mom how much it will cost when they deliver.

_____

_____

_____

☐ 2. Call an older family member, like your grandmother or an aunt/uncle. Before you make the call, brainstorm some questions you can ask first. Try to spend at least 20 minutes having a conversation.

☐ 3. Call the Denver Public Library – Listen to the options and choose the story that is best for you! Phone-a-Story: +1-720-865-8500

☐ 4. Call a friend to invite them over for a play date. Check with your parents first for permission and to confirm when would be a good time.

Friend's Name _____

Time and Date of Playdate: _____

_____

Practice writing your parents' phone numbers below. Memorize these numbers in case you ever need to reach them.

MAZE: Which telephone leads to the base? Color the wires to find out.

Skill #5 –
How to Write a
Thank You Card

Think of three people in your life who live outside of your home, whom you could thank for something. Follow these steps to write and send thank you cards to them!

Writing a thank you card is an important skill that you will need as an adult.

It's important to send thank you cards in the following circumstances:
- When someone gives you a birthday present or other gift
- To an employer who gives you a promotion at work
- To a friend who helps you with a project
- To an adult who teaches you a new skill
- Whenever someone does something kind or thoughtful that goes beyond what is expected of them

Write down the names here of who you will write to:

1. _____

2. _____

3. _____

Step One: Buy or create a thank you card that is appropriate for the person you are sending it to.

A brightly colored, glitter filled card is perfect for thanking Grandma for the birthday gift she sent you; but duller colors and clear print will look more professional for thanking your piano teacher for giving you lessons this year. Consider the person who will be receiving the card and what is appropriate for them.

Step Two: Write the thank you note.

- Address the card with "Dear _____," in the top left corner.
- Be specific about what you are thankful for. For example, instead of saying, "Thanks for being my teacher," say, "Thank you for teaching me how to bake muffins."
- Explain how what they have done will benefit you and why you are thankful. For example, "Now that I know how to crochet, I will be able to make beanies for all my friends as Christmas presents this year."
- End your note by saying "thank you" one more time, acknowledging the person's character.

Examples:
"Thank you so much for your generosity."
"Thank you for your thoughtfulness to remember me on my birthday."
"Thank you for being patient with me."
"Thank you for giving me the opportunity to learn something new."

Use the spaces below to practice what you will write,
then ask your parents to check for spelling or grammar
mistakes before copying the final version into your card.
Use your very best handwriting!

Step Three: Address and mail your card

Follow this pattern to address an envelope correctly. Be sure to include a stamp on the upper right hand corner of your envelope. Seal your envelope with the thank you card inside and feel free to add stickers or other decorations to the envelope if you'd like. Then, take your completed cards to the Post Office or drop them in the mail slot.

Sender's Full Name
Street Address
City, State, Zip Code

Receiver's Full Name
Street Address
City, State, Zip Code

Practice what you will write below and have your parent check for mistakes, then copy onto a real envelope.

Skill #6 –
How to Make a Meal Plan

Creating a meal plan is a very helpful tool when you are in charge of preparing food. Having a plan will help ensure that you have all the needed supplies on hand, and will help you eat healthy, balanced meals. Follow these steps to create a week-long meal plan for your family.

Write down examples of foods that could fit in each of these different food groups:

PROTEINS	CARBOHYDRATES	FATS

BREAKFAST

Starting with breakfast, brainstorm all the meals your family enjoys eating (ask family members to contribute ideas). Make sure there is protein in every meal, and feel free to add on other carbohydrates (like bread products, fruit or honey) and/or fats (butter, avocado, or coconut oil). Add in vegetables where you can! Draw seven different breakfast options on the plates below.

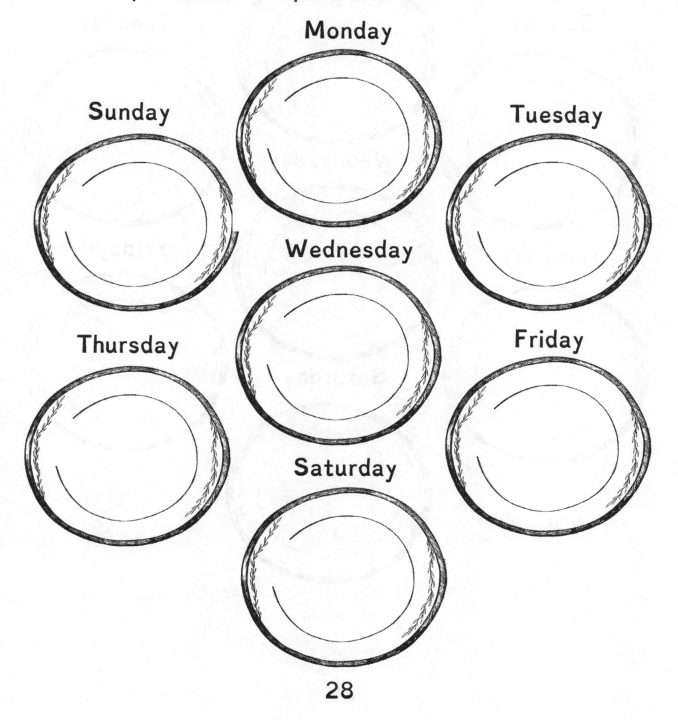

Monday

Sunday

Tuesday

Wednesday

Thursday

Friday

Saturday

LUNCH

Brainstorm all your family's favorite lunches and then choose seven to draw below. Start with a protein, add on some vegetables, and then add other foods.

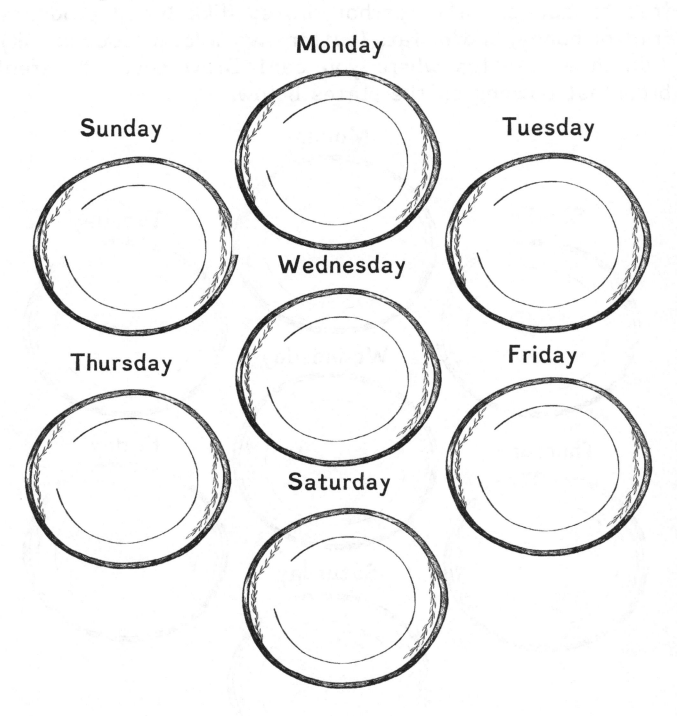

Monday

Sunday

Tuesday

Wednesday

Thursday

Friday

Saturday

DINNER

Draw seven of your family's favorite dinners below. Start with protein, add on vegetables, and then add other foods.

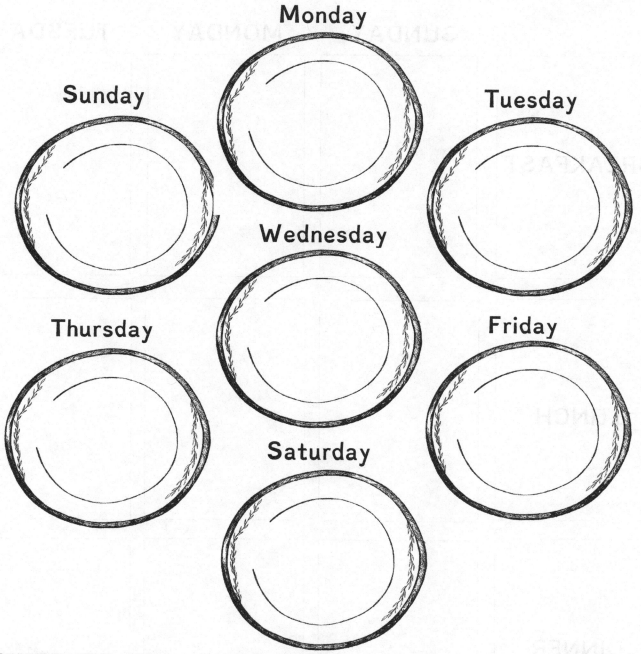

Monday

Sunday

Tuesday

Wednesday

Thursday

Friday

Saturday

DINNER TIP: Can you categorize your dinners into groups? If so, it can be helpful to create themes for different weeknights. For example, Mondays: Asian cuisine, Tuesdays: Tacos, Wednesdays: Casseroles, etc. You can repeat breakfasts and lunches but have multiple different weekly meal plans for dinners.

WRITE YOUR
MEAL PLAN BELOW

	SUNDAY	MONDAY	TUESDAY
BREAKFAST			
LUNCH			
DINNER			

WRITE YOUR
MEAL PLAN BELOW

WEDNESDAY	THURSDAY	FRIDAY	SATURDAY

Skill #7 –
How to Write a Shopping List

Now that you have a weekly meal plan, it's time to write your shopping list to make sure you'll have all the food on hand you need to prepare the meals. Go back to your plan on the previous page and think about which ingredients you'll need to make each meal. Then, add the ingredients, with the amount you'll need next to it, in each category.

PRODUCE (Fruits/Vegetables...)

MEAT (Chicken, Ground Beef, Bacon...)

DAIRY (Milk, Cheese, Yogurt...)

GRAINS (Bread, Tortillas, Oats...)

CANNED/DRY FOODS (Beans, Rice, Lentils, Canned Corn...)

CONDIMENTS/SPICES (Ketchup, Mustard, Salt, Pepper, Cumin, Basil...)

OILS/SWEETENERS (Olive Oil, Honey, Maple Syrup...)

Now that you know what you'll NEED – go check your kitchen/pantry and see what you already have on hand. Cross off any items that you already have.

Skill #8 –
Public Speaking

Use your resources to find some tips about public speaking! Write down the tips you learn below:

_____

_____

_____

_____

_____

_____

_____

_____

_____

_____

_____

_____

_____

_____

_____

_____

_____

_____

Try these games to practice public speaking. Put a check mark next to each one you complete! (If you can find someone to watch you, great! If not, just do the activities by yourself or on video).

☐ 1. Pick an object you have at home and create a 3 minute commercial of yourself selling it! Set an alarm; your challenge is to talk for the full 3 minutes without pausing. If you can't do it on the first try, try again.

☐ 2. Pretend that you know the definitions of these crazy words. Once again, you goal is keep talking and convince your listeners that you know what you are talking about. Spend one minute on each definition. Speak with confidence! When you're done, you can look up the real defintions.

- gongoozle
- cockamamie
- tatterdemalion
- flumadiddle
- bumfuzzle
- cattywampus

☐ 3. Think of something you know how to do that you could teach to others. Make a video of yourself giving instructions. Use all the tips you learned about public speaking!

Find a video of a famous speech to watch. Make observations about what the speaker does and take notes using the prompts below.

Title of Speech:

_____

Speaker:

_____

Where did the speaker look while giving their speech?

☐ At the floor   ☐ At their notes   ☐ At the audience

Did the speaker talk quickly or slowly? Loudly or quietly? Could you understand what they were saying?

_____

_____

_____

What sort of emotions did the speaker express in the way they spoke? Circle all that apply.

Passion   No emotion
Anger   Happiness
Excitement   Hopefulness
Compassion   Fear

TONGUE TWISTERS

Write down five tongue twisters. See how many times you can say each one before making a mistake! This will help you practice enunciating (speaking clearly) your words, a skill you need to be a good public speaker!

1._____
_____
_____
_____

2._____
_____
_____
_____

3._____
_____
_____
_____

4._____
_____
_____
_____

5._____
_____
_____
_____

That's Not Appropriate!

Public speaking doesn't require fancy clothing, but you do need to demonstrate that you care. Color in the clothing that would be appropriate to wear while giving a speech, and put an X over inappropriate clothing.

If you had the opportunity to present a speech to the President of the United States, explaining something that was important to you, what would you choose to talk about? Draw a picture of yourself below giving the speech.

Title of your speech

_____

Skill #9 –
How to be a Good Friend

What sort of characteristics do good friends have?
Circle all that apply.

A good friend is....

Honest

Teases you about your weaknesses

Trustworthy

Kind

Shares their things with you

Invites you to hang out with them

Talks about themselves all the time

Listens without interrupting

Supportive of your different interests

Happy for you when something good happens in your life

Keeps promises

Write down the names of some of the friends you have.

_____

_____

_____

_____

_____

What are some things your friends do that make them a good friend to you? Draw a picture below of a real life example.

Can you think of anybody you know who doesn't have many friends? Is there someone who is always by themselves during sports, at a park, at church, etc?

The best way to HAVE a friend is to BE a friend

Write down some names of people you could befriend – and write an idea for each of them of something kind you could do to initiate a friendship.

1.

2.

3.

4.

5.

TIP: Don't be discouraged if your first few attempts at friendships don't work out – it takes a while to figure out who you "click" with. Just keep trying!

Color this picture of friends spending time together.

Skill #10 –
How to Be Safe Online

Use your resources to find out – what are the potential dangers of being online? Define each of these terms:

Malware –

Online Frauds/Scams –

Sexual Predators –

Inappropriate/Dangerous websites –

Cyberbullying –

Write a list of rules about how to stay safe on the Internet.

1.

2.

3.

4.

5.

6.

7.

8.

SCREEN TIME DANGERS

Let's imagine that you are able to safely navigate the Internet and avoid many of the dangers we've discovered. Even so, what could be the harm of spending too much time online, even if it was time spent safely?

Research articles or videos to help you find some answers and write what you learn below.

1.

2.

3.

HIDDEN PICTURES
Can you find the hidden pictures below?

Skill #11 –
How to Make Your Bed

Why is it important to make your bed everyday? Use your resources and find out three reasons:

1.

2.

3.

Watch some videos about how to make a bed and decide which method will work best for **YOUR** bed.

Draw pictures of the steps you will take to make your bed.

STEP ONE

STEP TWO

STEP THREE

STEP FOUR

Draw a picture below of what your finished bed should look like.

Make a habit of making your bed every day when you wake up! Try to do it everyday for the next ten days. Color a bed for each day you make your bed.

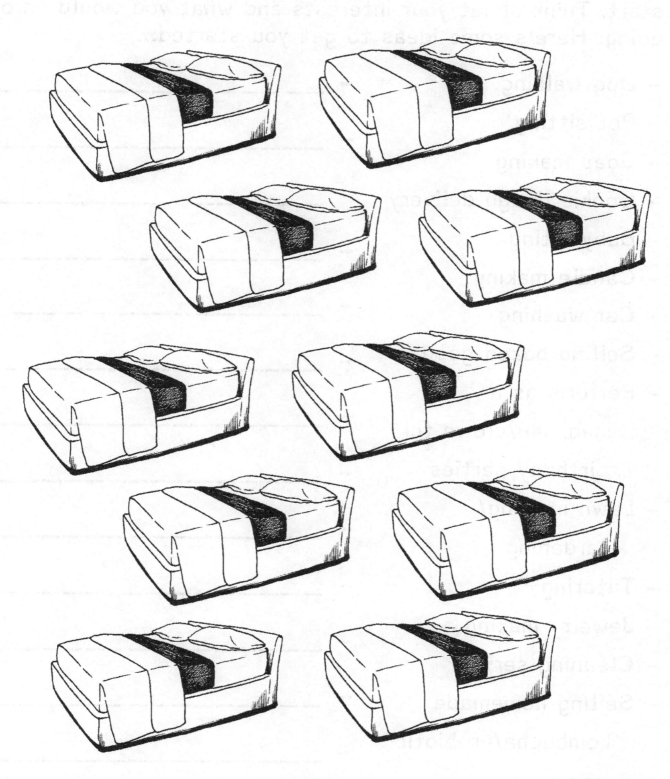

Skill #12 –
How to Start a Small Business

Brainstorm some ideas about possible businesses you could start. Think about your interests and what you would enjoy doing. Here's some ideas to get you started...

- Dog walking
- Pet sitting
- Soap making
- Cookie dough delivery
- Babysitting
- Candle making
- Car washing
- Selling baked goods
- Perform as a magician/clown for birthday parties
- Lawn mowing/ gardening
- Tutoring
- Jewelry making
- Cleaning service
- Selling homemade kombucha/probiotic sodas

- _____
- _____
- _____
- _____
- _____
- _____
- _____
- _____
- _____
- _____
- _____

55

Research the legal requirements to have a small business in your city/state. Write them down below, and keep track of how this would affect your expenses (the cost of operating your business).

_____
_____
_____
_____
_____
_____
_____
_____
_____
_____

Speaking of Expenses....
What would you need to spend to get started? Think about all the supplies/materials/help you would need, and keep track here.

_____	$_____
_____	$_____
_____	$_____
_____	$_____
_____	$_____
_____	$_____
_____	$_____
_____	$_____
_____	$_____
_____	$_____
TOTAL	$_____

Research some tips about how to provide good customer service. Write down what you learn below.

1.

2.

3.

4.

What will you name your business?
Brainstorm some ideas below and then circle the one you like the best.

ADVERTISING

Where will you advertise your business? Create a flyer below that you could make copies of to hand out to potential customers.

Watch out for the counterfeit bills! Can you look closely and only color the REAL dollar bills green? If you spot a fake, put a red X on it.

If you decide to start your business, use this page to keep track of your profits.

Skill #13 – Food Storage

Research these different methods for preserving food, define them below:

Canning –

Fermentation –

Drying –

Fermented Foods

Taking care of a ferment is similar to caring for a pet. You will need to learn how to "feed" it and keep it safe from mold or spoiling. Pick one of these foods to try making at home!

Pickles
Sourdough Bread
Sauerkraut
Fermented Ginger Soda

Fermented Carrots
Milk Kefir
Kombucha Soda
Yogurt

Circle the one you are going to try. Then research how to do it. Write notes below about the steps you will take.

1.

2.

3.

4.

5.

How long will your fermented food last in the fridge?

_____

Use a piece of masking tape and add an expiration date to your product!

Research how long each of these foods lasts in the pantry, fridge and freezer:

	Pantry	Fridge	Freezer
Ground Beef (uncooked)			
Chicken (uncooked)			
Pork (uncooked)			
Raw milk			
Pasteurized milk			
Cream Cheese			
Sour Cream			
Butter (pasteurized)			
Yogurt			
Banana			
Melon			
Blueberry			
Pineapple			
Mayonnaise			
Ketchup			

	Pantry	Fridge	Freezer
Strawberry			
Lettuce			
Tomato			
Cucumber			
Spinach			
Broccoli			
Potato			
Green Beans			
Corn on the Cob			
Rice (uncooked)			
Rice (cooked)			
Beans (uncooked)			
Beans (cooked)			
Lentils			
Avocado			
Peanuts			
Squash			

Skill #14 –
Meeting New People

Where are some places you might meet new people?

Neighborhood park
Grocery store
Sports Team
Church
Volunteering

_____
_____
_____
_____
_____

TIPS FOR MEETING NEW PEOPLE:

- One of the easiest ways to connect with a new person is to find something that you have in common. Sometimes you can observe to figure out similarities and then comment on them, and sometimes you will need to ask questions to figure it out.

- As you observe a new person, look for something on which you can compliment them. Be kind, and be sure to smile. (Example: "your dog is so cute!" or "that's a really cool skateboard").

- Be interested in the other person: ask questions and then look for social cues to see how they react. If they enjoy answering your questions, ask more. If they become uncomfortable, try sharing something about yourself instead.

- Remember to always introduce yourself (tell them your name and ask for theirs) within the first few minutes of chatting with someone new.

Write down what you could say in each of these situations....

You're at the grocery store and you notice another kid wearing a t-shirt with your favorite band on it.

At the park, you notice another kid being kind and helpful to your younger sibling.

At soccer practice, there's a kid who is very shy and doesn't ever talk or look at anyone else. What could you say to help them feel more comfortable?

A new kid shows up to your Sunday School class.

Write down some examples of questions you could ask each of these people if you met them in real life.

Now go out and give it a try! Meet three new people and write what you learn about them here. Draw their picture in the box and be sure to write down their name so you won't forget it.

Name _____

What you learned

Name _____

What you learned

Name _____

What you learned

Skill #15 –
How to Clean a Bathroom

First, watch some videos to learn some tips!

_____
_____
_____
_____
_____
_____
_____
_____
_____

What sort of things should be done DAILY to keep a bathroom clean?

_____
_____
_____
_____
_____
_____
_____
_____
_____
_____

What sort of things should be done WEEKLY to keep a bathroom clean?

_____
_____
_____
_____
_____
_____
_____
_____
_____
_____

Write down steps about how
to clean the toilet:

1.

2.

3.

4.

5.

Write down steps about how to clean the
shower/bathtub:

1.

2.

3.

4.

5.

CROSSWORD PUZZLE

Can you remember the names of these bathroom items?

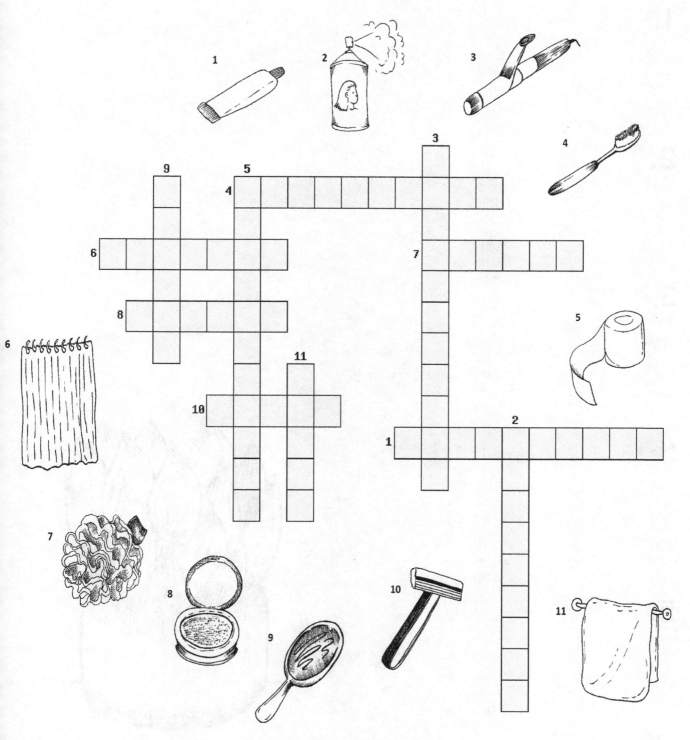

Skill #16 –
How to Care for a House Plant

First, let's research. What are the benefits of owning a house plant?

1.

2.

3.

4.

5.

What are the best types of indoor plants?
Pick three and draw their pictures below.

Name: _____

Name: _____

Name: _____

Go visit a local nursery and pick out a plant that you can take care of by yourself. Ask for specific instructions about how to care for it or research when you get home.

Write down the instructions here. How often does it need to be watered? How much sunlight will it need?

_____

_____

_____

_____

_____

_____

_____

_____

_____

_____

_____

_____

_____

_____

_____

_____

_____

MAZE
Find your way to the center of the vines!

START

FINISH

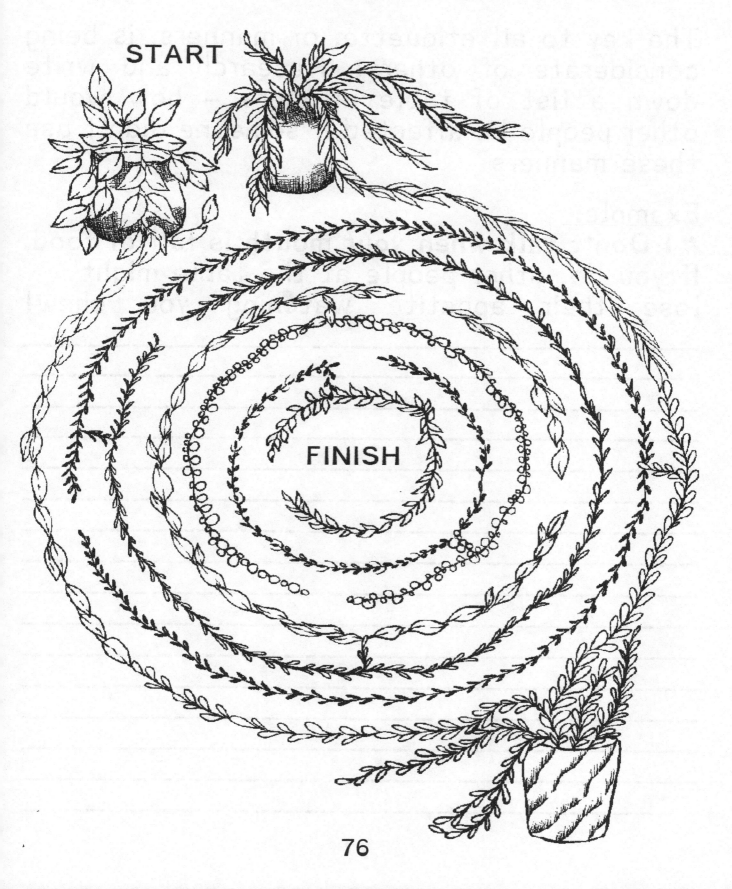

Skill #17 -
Table Manners

The key to all etiquette, or manners, is being considerate of others! Research and write down a list of table manners - how would other people be affected if someone didn't use these manners?

Example:
#1 Don't talk when your mouth is full of food. If you do, other people at the table might lose their appetite watching you chew!

_____
_____
_____
_____
_____
_____
_____
_____
_____
_____
_____
_____
_____
_____

Circle the pictures of good manners. Cross out the pictures of bad table manners.

How to Set the Table
Draw a meal on each plate.

MANNERS QUIZ

Pick one meal to practice your perfect table manners. Give yourself points accordingly.

Come to the table with clean hands and face	+ 10 points
Stay in your seat the whole meal	+ 10 points
Place your napkin in your lap when you sit down	+ 10 points
Ask, "May you please pass..." when you need something	+ 10 points
Reaching across the table	– 5 points
Interrupting or making loud noises	– 5 points
Ask to be excused from the table when you finish	+ 5 points
Keep your cup, silverware, napkin in their proper places during the meal	+ 10 points
Say, "Thank You" to the cook	+ 5 points
Elbows or other body parts on the table	– 5 points
Complaining about the food	– 15 points
Ask someone at the table a question to encourage conversation	+ 10 points

YOUR SCORE = _____

Show your work here

If you scored...
More than 70 points – you made Emily Post proud
50–70 points – back to Finishing School
Less than 50 points – apologize to your mother

Skill #18 –
How to use an Iron

What are some benefits of ironing clothing? Use your resources to find out and make a list below.

_____
_____
_____
_____
_____
_____
_____
_____
_____
_____
_____
_____

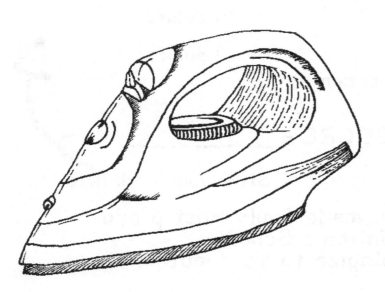

Research some safety tips about using an iron.

1.

2.

3.

4.

5.

Connect the dots to draw an iron!

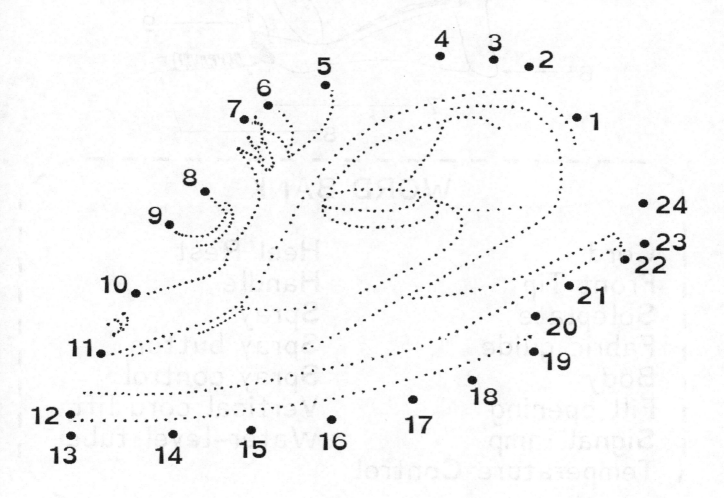

Identify the parts of an iron

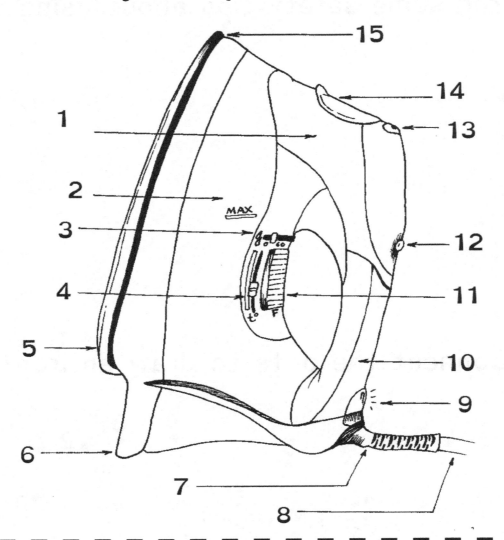

Match the words in the word bank to where each number points on the picture.

1. _____
2. _____
3. _____
4. _____
5. _____
6. _____
7. _____
8. _____
9. _____
10. _____
11. _____
12. _____
13. _____
14. _____
15. _____

Watch a video about how to iron, then give it a try! If your family doesn't own an iron, see if you can borrow one from a neighbor. Put a check mark next to each item you practice ironing.

☐ Pillowcase

☐ Collared shirt

☐ Pants

☐ Towels

84

Skill #19 –
How to Use a Dictionary

A dictionary is a useful tool to help you understand the meaning of a word, how it is used in speech, and how to pronounce it correctly.

The first step to using a dictionary is being able to find the word you are looking for. Dictionaries are organized according to ALPHABETICAL ORDER.

Can you put these words in alphabetical order? Use your resources to learn how if you have any questions.

Horseradish	Quilt
Question	Sponge
Satchel	Physical
Kangaroo	Fantastic
Island	Puzzle
Paparazzi	Peanut

1.
2.
3.
4.
5.
6.
7.
8.
9.
10.
11.
12.

A dictionary entry will always tell you what part of speech the word is. Define and give an example of each type of word.

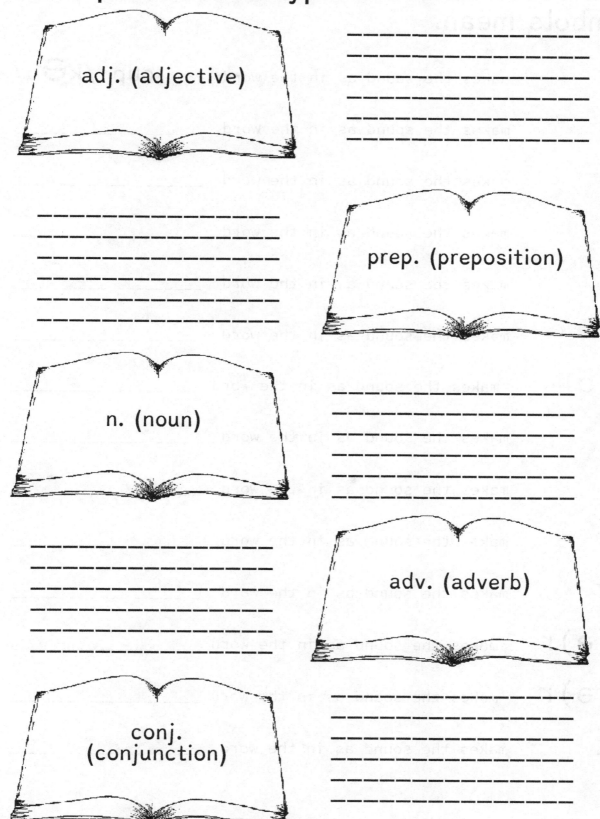

adj. (adjective)

_____
_____
_____
_____
_____

_____
_____
_____
_____
_____

prep. (preposition)

n. (noun)

_____
_____
_____
_____
_____

_____
_____
_____
_____
_____

adv. (adverb)

conj. (conjunction)

_____
_____
_____
_____
_____

Open up a dictionary and you will see a pronunciation guide next to each word. Use your resources to find out what each of these symbols mean.

ə   makes the sound as in the word   cup /kəp/

i   makes the sound as in the word _____

ɪ   makes the sound as in the word _____

ɛ   makes the sound as in the word _____

æ   makes the sound as in the word _____

ɑ   makes the sound as in the word _____

ɔ,ɑ   makes the sound as in the word _____

ʊ   makes the sound as in the word _____

u   makes the sound as in the word _____

ɔr   makes the sound as in the word _____

ər   makes the sound as in the word _____

ɪ(ə)r   makes the sound as in the word _____

ɛ(ə)r   makes the sound as in the word _____

eɪ   makes the sound as in the word _____

87

aɪ   makes the sound as in the word   _____

aʊ   makes the sound as in the word   _____

oʊ   makes the sound as in the word   _____

ɔɪ   makes the sound as in the word   _____

æ   makes the sound as in the word   _____

ɑ   makes the sound as in the word   _____

dʒ   makes the sound as in the word   _____

ð   makes the sound as in the word   _____

h   makes the sound as in the word   _____

j   makes the sound as in the word   _____

ŋ   makes the sound as in the word   _____

ʃ   makes the sound as in the word   _____

tʃ   makes the sound as in the word   _____

θ   makes the sound as in the word   _____

z   makes the sound as in the word   _____

ʒ   makes the sound as in the word   _____

Can you write the pronunciation of your name here? /_____/

Flip through a dictionary and find three new words. Write the word in the box. Write the definitions below. Also, copy down the pronunciation and type of speech for each word.

/_____/

Part of speech:

_____

Definition:

- - - - - - - - - - - - - - - - - - - -
- - - - - - - - - - - - - - - - - - - -
- - - - - - - - - - - - - - - - - - - -

/_____/

Part of speech:

_____

Definition:

- - - - - - - - - - - - - - - - - - - -
- - - - - - - - - - - - - - - - - - - -
- - - - - - - - - - - - - - - - - - - -

/_____/

Part of speech:

_____

Definition:

- - - - - - - - - - - - - - - - - - - -
- - - - - - - - - - - - - - - - - - - -
- - - - - - - - - - - - - - - - - - - -

BONUS: A thesaurus can help you find synonyms (words with the same meaning) to make your writing more interesting.

Use a thesaurus to find synonyms for the three new words you just learned.

Example:

said

Synonyms:
spoke
commented
mentioned
screamed
whispered
replied
proclaimed
remarked
yelled
exclaimed
murmured
stammered
explained
responded
argued
suggested

Synonyms:
_____
_____
_____

Synonyms:
_____
_____
_____

Synonyms:
_____
_____
_____

Skill #20 –
Change a Lightbulb

Use your resources to make a list of safety tips for changing light bulbs.

1.

2.

3.

4.

5.

6.

7.

8.

Define these terms:

hot swapping:

----

voltage:

----

incandescent:

----

fluorescent:

Where should you put an old light bulb after you've replaced it?

How should you change a broken lightbulb?

What are some warning signs that a light bulb might need to be changed soon?

Solve the puzzle to find a tip to help you when you're changing light bulbs.

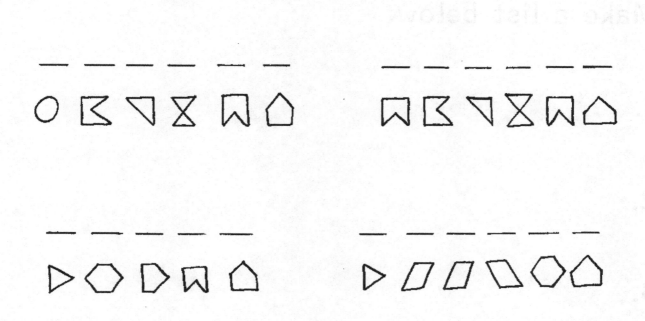

Answer: RIGHTY TIGHTY, LEFTY LOOSEY

Skill #21 –
How to Apologize

What are some reasons why you might need to apologize to someone?

Make a list below.

1.

2.

3.

4.

5.

When was the last time you had to apologize for something?

What are the elements of a perfect apology? Use your resources to learn some tips and then write what you find below.

Solve the puzzle below to learn the one word you should NEVER include in an apology.

Instructions: Multiply each number. Then match each answer to the letter in the Alphabet Key. Write the letter on the blank above the problem number.

1	2	3	4	5
6 x 7	5 x 4	3 x 2	6 x 3	4 x 7

6	7	8	9	10
6 x 4	5 x 3	3 x 7	7 x 9	4 x 8

11	12	13	14	15
6 x 2	5 x 9	6 x 9	9 x 1	4 x 9

16	17	18	19	20
6 x 5	5 x 1	3 x 9	2 x 5	4 x 1

____ ____ ____ ____ ____   ____ ____ ____
20   3   14   3   19   4   2   9

" ____ ____ ____ "
6   16   12

Alphabet Key:

A = 20	E = 6	I = 28	M = 0	Q = 15	U = 30
B = 24	F = 36	J = 21	N = 4	R = 10	V = 9 Y = 63
C = 12	G = 27	K = 32	O = 44	S = 18	W = 2 Z = 25
D = 42	H = 5	L = 54	P = 39	T = 45	X = 8

Other than using the words, "I'm sorry" what are some other ways to apologize?

_____

_____

_____

_____

_____

_____

_____

_____

_____

Skill #22 -
How to Study for a Test

Use your resources to find tips about studying skills. Write down what you learn below.

MNEMONICS

What are mnemonics?

_____
_____
_____
_____
_____

Research **3** different mnemonic strategies
and give examples of each below:

1. _____

2. _____

3. _____

TIPS for SPELLING TESTS

Write down **10** words below to practice spelling. Then we will use some fun strategies to help you learn them!

1. _____   6. _____
2. _____   7. _____
3. _____   8. _____
4. _____   9. _____
5. _____   10. _____

TIP #1 – Write your words again, but this time, put a hyphen (-) between each of the syllables. This helps you to think about the word in parts. (Example: hel-i-cop-ter)

1. _____   6. _____
2. _____   7. _____
3. _____   8. _____
4. _____   9. _____
5. _____   10. _____

TIP #2 – Play a game of hangman with your spelling words! Hand your spelling list to a parent or sibling who can set up the game for you on a separate piece of paper. Give yourself seven chances to guess each word (the hangman's head, body, two arms, two legs and face!)

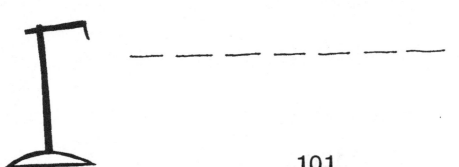

TIP #3 –
Create your own wordsearch with your spelling words! Here is an empty wordsearch grid. Write in each of your spelling words – they can go forward, backward, up, down, or diagonal. When you're done, fill in all the empty squares with a variety of letters. You can make it tricky by purposefully spelling a word incorrectly in the empty squares, or by spelling only half of a word. When you're done, ask someone else to complete your wordsearch!

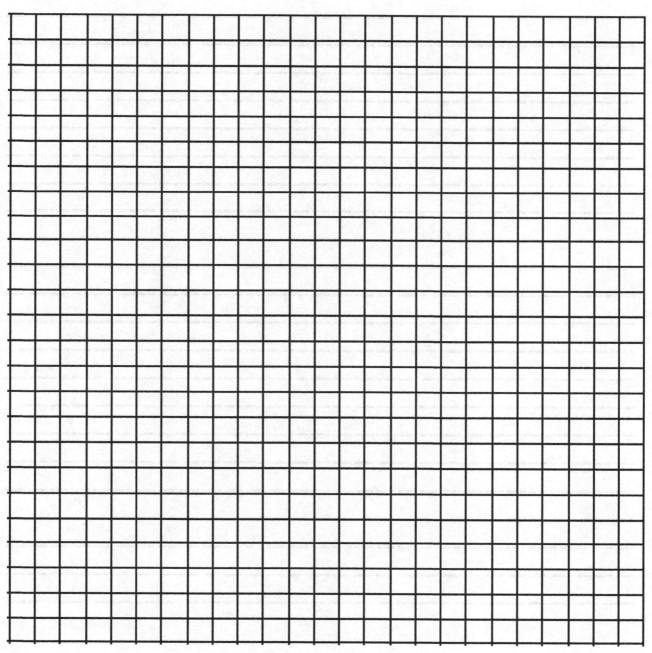

Skill #23 -
How to Manage Your Time

Time management is learning how to use your time well; so that you can accomplish all the things you need to get done and have time left over for fun!

Let's start by watching some videos or reading books with tips on time management. Write what you learn below.

To practice this skill, let's start by making a to-do list and schedule for your morning activities. Once you master this chunk of time, consider doing the same for other parts of your day as well.

Write a To-Do List for all the things you need to accomplish in the morning. Be specific (instead of "clean room", list specific things like "make bed, pick up dirty laundry, put toys away, put books away, straighten rug" etc).

☐   ☐

☐   ☐

☐   ☐

☐   ☐

☐   ☐

☐   ☐

☐   ☐

☐   ☐

Next, starting with the time you wake up in the morning, make a plan for when you will accomplish each of your tasks.

6:00am

6:15am

6:30am

6:45am

7:00am

7:15am

7:30am

7:45am

8:00am

8:15am

8:30am

8:45am

9:00am

9:15am

9:30am

9:45am

10:00am

WATCH THE CLOCK

As you are doing your tasks, it is important to have a clock nearby at all times so that you can check to see that you are sticking to your schedule. If you find that you've given yourself too much or too little time for certain tasks, adjust your schedule accordingly.

Number the clock face and draw in the hour hand and minute hand to show the time you usually wake up.

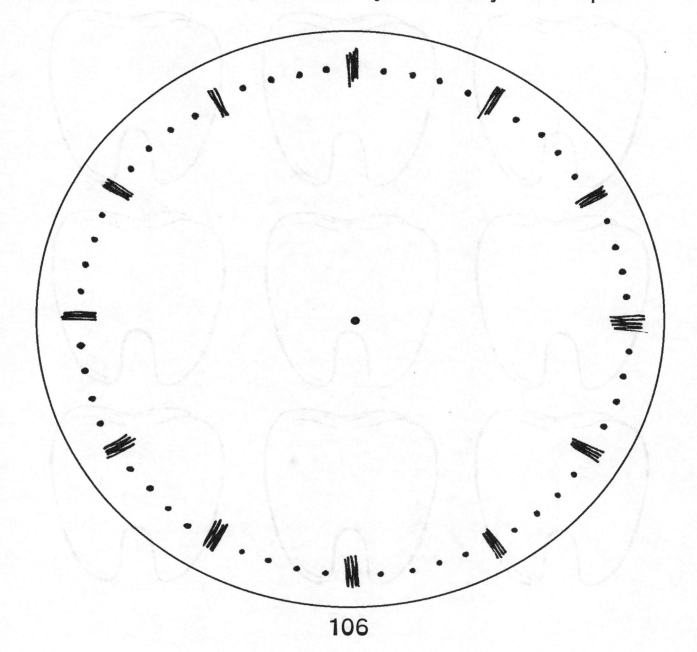

Skill #24 –
How to Take Care of Your Teeth

Did you know that if you had the perfect diet, you wouldn't need to brush your teeth to avoid cavities? Use your resources to learn which foods **SHOULD** and **SHOULD NOT** be in your diet to keep your teeth healthy.

FOODS FOR HEALTHY TEETH

Draw pictures or write the names of foods that build strong teeth.

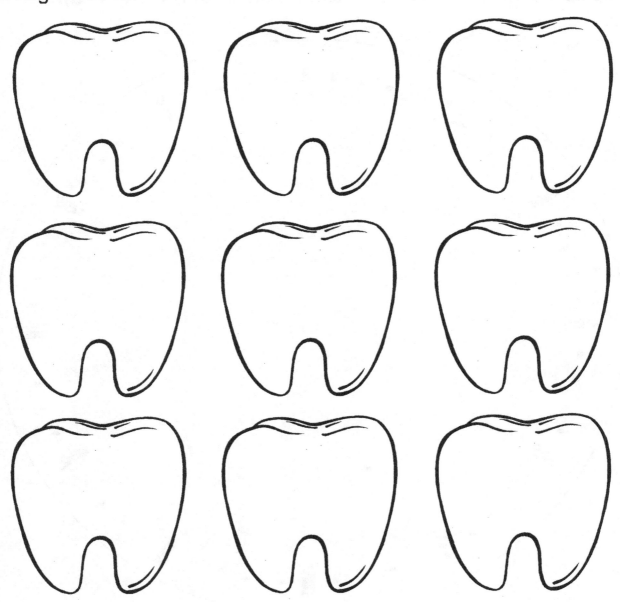

FOODS TO AVOID

_____   _____
_____   _____
_____   _____
_____   _____
_____   _____
_____   _____
_____   _____
_____   _____

Research **PHYTIC ACID** in relation to dental health –
what is it? Which foods contain it? How can you remove
or reduce it in your food?

_____
_____
_____
_____
_____

Who was Weston A. Price? What is he famous for?

_____
_____
_____
_____
_____
_____
_____
_____
_____
_____

Use your resources to find information about how to heal cavities. Take notes on what you learn below.

Write the definition of remineralization (in relation to dental health):

Even if you had a perfect diet, it's still a good idea to brush your teeth regularly! Keeping your mouth clean will ensure you have good breath.

Watch some videos about how to brush your teeth properly and write down some steps to follow below.

1.

2.

3.

4.

5.

What is flouride?

_____
_____
_____
_____

Write a list of the pros and cons of using flouride in toothpaste:

PROS   CONS

_____   _____
_____   _____
_____   _____
_____   _____
_____   _____
_____   _____

Skill #25 -
How to Use a Tape Measure

Watch a video and learn some pro tips about how to use a tape measure. Write down what you learn below.

_____
_____
_____
_____
_____
_____
_____
_____
_____
_____
_____
_____
_____
_____
_____
_____
_____
_____
_____

Label this tape measure accurately.

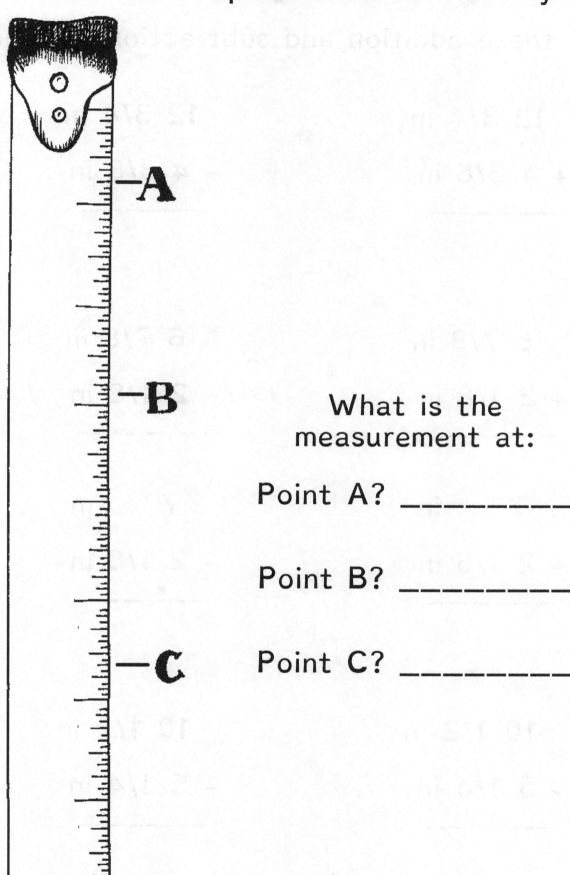

What is the
measurement at:

Point A? _____

Point B? _____

Point C? _____

Measuring Math

Solve these addition and subtraction problems.

12 3/4 in   12 3/4 in

+ 4 3/8 in   - 4 3/8 in

———————   ———————

6 7/8 in   6 7/8 in

+ 2 1/8 in   - 2 1/8 in

———————   ———————

7   in   7   in

+ 2 1/8 in   - 2 1/8 in

———————   ———————

10 1/2 in   10 1/2 in

+ 5 1/4 in   - 5 1/4 in

———————   ———————

Measure the height of everyone in your family. If you were to stand on each other's heads, how tall would your family be?

My height: _____

+ _____

+ _____

+ _____

+ _____

+ _____

+ _____

TOTAL
Height of My Family: _____

114

Skill #26 –
How to Schedule an Appointment

When are some times when you might need to schedule an appointment? Write your ideas on the blank lines.

- Doctor   _____
- Dentist   _____
- Hair cut   _____
- DMV   _____
- Nail salon   _____
- Consultation with an expert   _____
- Dinner reservation   _____
- Play date with a friend   _____
- Chiropractor   _____
- Massage   _____
- Job interview   _____

Research some tips for making appointments and write them down below!

_____
_____
_____
_____
_____
_____
_____
_____
_____
_____
_____
_____

Pick three possible appointments from your list to practice what you've learned. Call and schedule your appointment. Then, write down the date and time of each appointment below, and also in your calendar so that you won't forget!

Virtual Appointments

Today many appointments happen virtually, and so it's important to be prepared and know the proper etiquette to attending a meeting online.

If you're not familiar with these video conferencing applications, create a pretend "meeting" in each of these and familiarize yourself with the different buttons and options. The time to practice is **NOT** during a real meeting, so spend plenty of time getting comfortable with each program before an actual appointment occurs. Check off each application that you practice using!

☐ Zoom   ☐ WhatsApp

☐ Google Meet   ☐ Marco Polo

☐ Skype   ☐ Houseparty

Watch some videos about video conferencing etiquette and make a list of rules below to follow.

1.

2.

3.

4.

5.

6.

7.

8.

9.

10.

Skill #27 – Read a Map

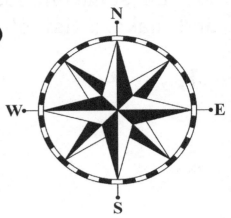

The first step to reading a map is learning how to read a compass

Do you know any mnemonics to help you remember the order of the cardinal directions? Create a few of your own. (Example: Never eat soggy waffles!)

N_____ E_____ S_____ W_____

N_____ E_____ S_____ W_____

It's important to develop spatial awareness – an understanding of where you are in relation to other things. Use the following activities to help you develop this skill.

#1 – Write the names of 5 places you visit regularly. When you are at each of these places, go outside and identify where North, East, South and West are. Use a compass or compass app on your parent's smartphone.

1. _____ ☐

2. _____ ☐

3. _____ ☐

4. _____ ☐

5. _____ ☐

119

#2 - Type your home address in Google Maps (on a computer). Zoom out until you can identify the different parts of your city, and find something you recognize in each direction. Use "Directions" and type in the names of parks, grocery stores, or other places you visit to identify where they are in relation to your home. Draw a map below with your home in the center and add as many points as you can to your map.

N

My house

W

E

S

#3 - Get a paper map of your city (bus stations, train stations and city hall are all good places to find maps) and copy the legend/key below.

Symbol	Meaning

#4 - Find your house on a city map and draw a star on it.

Look up the address to a restaurant in your town that you've never visited. Can you find it on the map? Using the paper map only, try to plan a route for how you would get there from your house. Write the directions you would take below. Your directions should state which cardinal direction you will be heading with each turn. For example, "Head west on Grand Ave. Turn left (south) onto 5th Street" Trace your route on your paper map. Then give your directions to your parents to see if they can find it!

Directions from my house to _____
(Name of Restaurant)

1. Start at _____
(Your address here)

2. Head _____

3. Turn _____ on _____

4.

5.

6.

7.

8.

9.

10.

Arrive at _____
(Restaurant's Address)

Skill #28 –
How to Make a Cup of Tea

Research the steps of making a perfect cup of tea, then draw pictures and write instructions below.

Research the caffeine content of these different types of teas, then put them in order from most caffeine to least.

MOST

——————

——————

——————

——————

——————

——————

——————

——————

——————

——————

——————

——————

LEAST

Green

White

Chai

Rooibos

Chamomile

Mint

Earl Grey

Ginger

English Breakfast

Black

Oolong

Dandelion

Fruit Teas
(Peach, Raspberry, Mango, etc)

Host a Tea Party

Now that you know how to make a cup of tea, research some tips about how to throw a tea party and invite some friends or family members to join you!

Write the plans for your party below:

Date _____

Time _____

Guest List:

_____   _____

_____   _____

_____   _____

_____   _____

MENU

Color the Tea Cups

Design your own tea cups:

Skill #29 –
How to Host a Garage Sale

A garage sale, or yard sale, is a great way to get rid of things you are no longer using and make some money at the same time. First, let's research some tips on how to make a garage sale successful.

Write what you learn below.

Decide when your garage sale will be and create flyers to hang up around your neighborhood to let others know.

Draw a design for your flyer below. Be sure to include what, where, when and list some categories of items you will have for sale (toys, clothing, electronics, etc).

Aside from hanging up flyers, you may want to place an ad in your local newspaper or on social media to attract more visitors.

Call your local newspaper to ask how to place an ad.

$$$ Prices $$$

Generally, items at a garage sale sell for about 1/4th (or less) of the price you bought them for. Decide ahead of time how much each item will cost, and make price tags for each item. Research how to price garage sale items and write what you learn below.

Kid clothing _____

Adult clothing _____

Shoes _____

Coats _____

Jewelry _____

Books _____

DVDs/CDs _____

Toys/Games _____

Furniture _____

Electronics _____

Bikes/Outdoor
Equipment _____

Baked goods _____

How much profit did your garage sale make? It's a good idea to have small bills on hand at the beginning to make change for people, but be sure to deduct that amount from your total at the end to find your profit.

Total Amount _____

Starting Cash - _____

Other Expenses - _____

Total Profit = _____

Draw a picture of what you will spend your profit on!

Skill #30 –
Give a Foot Massage

Did you know that the bottoms of your feet connect to other parts of your body, and that a good foot massage can help keep the whole body healthy? Giving a foot massage is a great skill to have to bless your friends and family members.

Research foot reflexology to discover which body parts connect to these different regions on the bottom of a foot.

WORD BANK

Neck
Brain
Sinus
Shoulder
Liver
Kidneys
Small Intestine
Sciatic Nerve
Gall Bladder
Spleen
Pancreas
Colon
Lungs
Pelvis
Heart
Eyes & Ears
Pituitary Gland
Bladder
Adrenal Glands

1. _____
2. _____
3. _____
4. _____
5. _____
6. _____
7. _____
8. _____
9. _____
10. _____
11. _____
12. _____
13. _____
14. _____
15. _____
16. _____
17. _____
18. _____
19. _____
20. _____

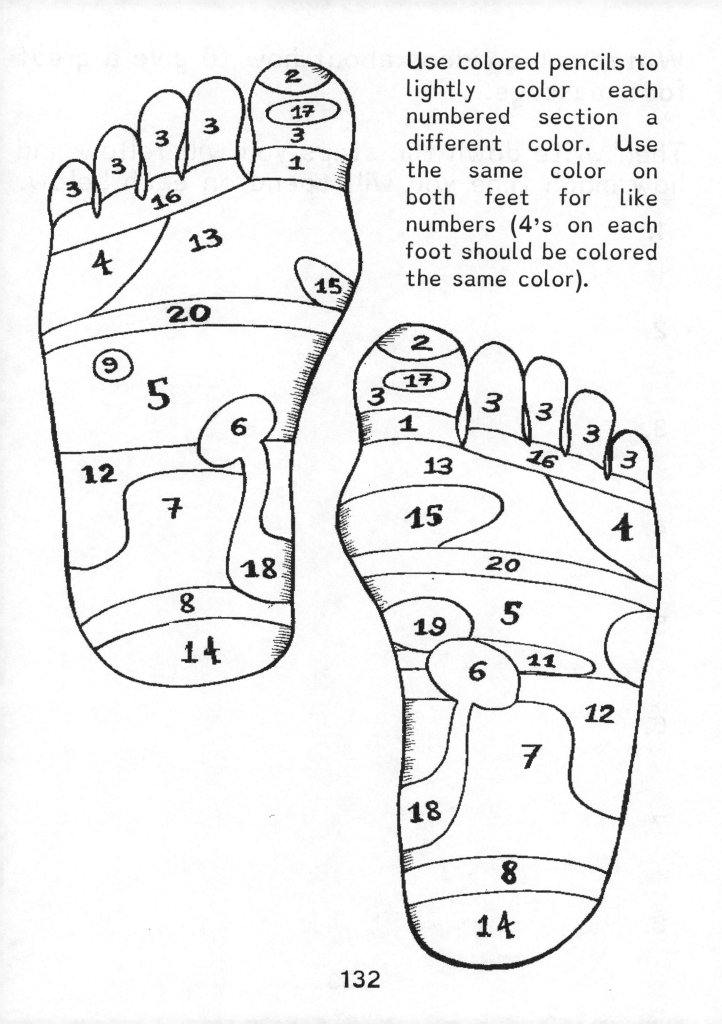

Use colored pencils to lightly color each numbered section a different color. Use the same color on both feet for like numbers (4's on each foot should be colored the same color).

Watch some videos about how to give a great foot massage.

Then write down the steps you will follow and how much time you will spend on each below.

1.

2.

3.

4.

5.

6.

7.

8.

An important part of becoming skilled at massage is listening to the feedback others give you. Practice your new skills on three friends/family members. Ask them for feedback and write down what they say here.

#1   Name: _____

Feedback:

_____
_____
_____
_____
_____

#2   Name: _____

Feedback:

_____
_____
_____
_____
_____

#3   Name: _____

Feedback:

_____
_____
_____
_____
_____

Skill #31 –
How to Find a Book in the Library

To find a book in the library, first you'll need to know what kind of book you're looking for. Write the differences below about these different types of books.

Non - Fiction

_____
_____
_____
_____
_____
_____

_____
_____
_____
_____
_____

Fiction

Biography

_____
_____
_____
_____
_____

_____
_____
_____
_____

Poetry

What is the Dewey Decimal System?

_____

_____

_____

_____

_____

_____

TRUE or FALSE – The Dewey Decimal System is used only to organize non-fiction books. _____

Which books fall into each of these categories?

000 - _____

100 - _____

200 - _____

300 - _____

400 - _____

500 - _____

600 - _____

700 - _____

800 - _____

900 - _____

Draw a map of YOUR city's library to help you remember how it is orgranized.

Write down the name of four books you have read or would like to read. Where would you find these in your library? Specify if they are non-fiction or fiction. Draw stars on your map to approximate where you would find them!

Title: _____

Author: _____

Fiction or Non-Fiction? _____

Where would you find it in your library?

_____

_____

Title: _____

Author: _____

Fiction or Non-Fiction? _____

Where would you find it in your library?

_____

_____

Title: _____

Author: _____

Fiction or Non-Fiction? _____

Where would you find it in your library?

_____

_____

Title: _____

Author: _____

Fiction or Non-Fiction? _____

Where would you find it in your library?

_____

_____

Skill #32 –
How to Tie a Tie

Tying a tie is an important skill for both males and females to have! Use your resources to learn how to tie a tie in these three different styles, and draw pictures of the steps you will take to create each one. Then practice until you can do each one well.

The ORIENTAL Knot

Step 1	Step 2	Step 3

Step 4	Step 5	Step 6

The FULL WINDSOR Knot

Step 1	Step 2	Step 3
Step 4	Step 5	Step 6

The FOUR-IN-HAND Knot

Step 1	Step 2	Step 3
Step 4	Step 5	Step 6

Which style
of tie would
be best for a
very formal
event?

_____

_____

Research to
learn more
about ties!

When would you
use a bow tie?

_____

_____

Make a list of
events in which it
would be necessary
to use a tie.

_____
_____
_____
_____
_____
_____
_____
_____
_____
_____
_____
_____
_____
_____
_____
_____
_____

Which style of
tie is best for
very tall men?

_____

_____

Fun Fact: What
do you call
someone who
collects ties?

_____

_____

Color the ties and design your own!

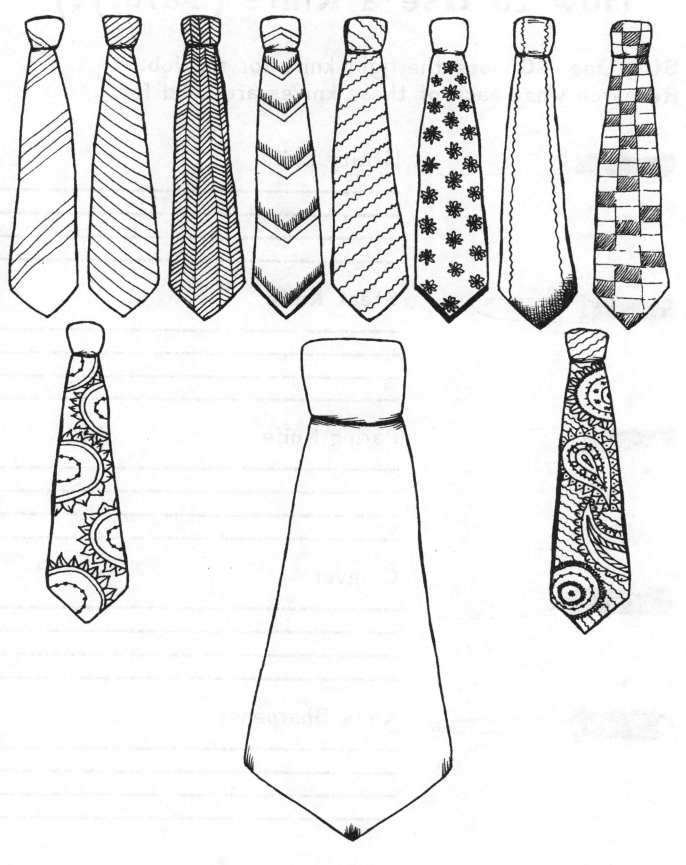

Skill #33 –
How to Use a Knife (Safely!)

Step One – Choose the right knife for the job.
Research what each of these knives are used for.

Utility Knife

_____
_____
_____
_____

Steak Knife

_____
_____
_____
_____

Paring Knife

_____
_____
_____
_____

Cleaver

_____
_____
_____
_____

Knife Sharpener

_____
_____
_____
_____

Santoku Knife

\- \-
\- \-
\- \-
\- \-

Chef's Knife

\- \-
\- \-
\- \-
\- \-

Boning Knife

\- \-
\- \-
\- \-
\- \-

Bread Knife

\- \-
\- \-
\- \-
\- \-

Carving Knife

\- \-
\- \-
\- \-
\- \-

(Circle the correct answer)
The safest knife is...

a **VERY SHARP KNIFE** or a **DULL KNIFE.**

Why?

\- \-
\- \-
\- \-
\- \-

Watch a video about knife safety and write down some tips you learn below!

1. _____

_____

_____

_____

2. _____

_____

_____

_____

3. _____

_____

_____

_____

4. _____

_____

_____

_____

Draw a picture of the kind of knife you would use to cut up a watermelon. What is that knife called?

_____

Research each of these types of cuts. Watch a video about how to do them. Draw a picture of each and then practice doing each one, using the safety tips you learned.
*Only use a knife with **SUPERVISION***

Small Dice

Medium Dice

Mince

Brunoise

Allumette

Batonette

Julienne

Chiffonade

Slice

Chop

Skill #34 –
Pump Gas in a Car

Watch some videos about how to pump your own gas in your car and write the steps below!

1. _____

_____

_____

2. _____

_____

_____

3. _____

_____

_____

4. _____

_____

_____

5. _____

_____

_____

6. _____

_____

_____

7. _____

_____

_____

What types of vehicles use **DIESEL** fuel?

_____
_____
_____
_____
_____
_____
_____

What would happen if you put diesel into a car that uses regular gasoline?

_____
_____
_____
_____
_____
_____
_____

How to calculate your car's gas mileage

When you go to the gas station, be sure to fill your gas tank all the way to full. Then, look on the car's mileage count and write down how many miles are on your car below:

Mileage #1

_____

The next time the gas tank is low and you go to refill at the gas station, take note of the mileage count again. Then subtract to find out how many miles your car drove in between gas refills. Also take note at the gas station how many gallons it took to refill your tank again.

Mileage #2 _____ Gallons used _____

How many gallons of gas did it take to fill the tank the second time?

Divide the number of miles driven by gallons used to find out how many miles your car can drive on each gallon of gasoline. Show your work below!

MPG Calculator	
Mileage #2	_____
minus –	
Mileage #1	_____
=	
TOTAL Miles Driven	_____
Divided by/ Gallons of gas needed to fill tank:	
	_____
= Miles per Gallon (MPG)	_____

Research to find the answers to these questions.

When is the best time to refill your gas tank?
_____

What can happen if you consistently let your gas tank get too close to empty?
_____
_____
_____

Measuring Gas

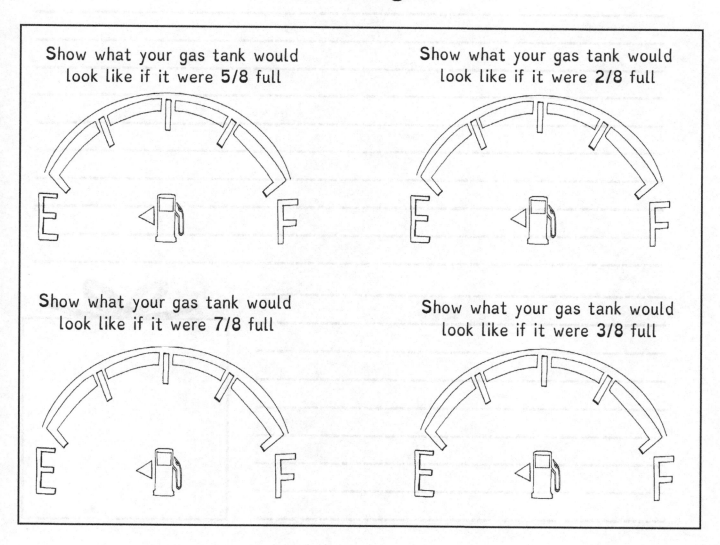

Show what your gas tank would look like if it were **5/8** full

Show what your gas tank would look like if it were **2/8** full

Show what your gas tank would look like if it were **7/8** full

Show what your gas tank would look like if it were **3/8** full

Skill #35 -
How to Wrap a Gift

Watch some videos about how to wrap a gift. Write down some tips you learn below:

_____
_____
_____
_____
_____
_____
_____
_____
_____
_____
_____
_____
_____
_____
_____
_____
_____
_____
_____
_____

Research each of these gift-wrapping methods. Draw a picture to help you remember how to do each one.

How to make a bag out of wrapping paper

How to make a bow from wrapping paper

How to wrap a gift when you don't have enough paper

Practice each of these new skills. When is the next time you will need to wrap a gift?

How to wrap a present without any tape

How to wrap a shoe box with lid

How to wrap a gift card

"It's not how much we give, but how much love we put into giving." — Mother Teresa

Research tips about how to be a good gift giver. Write what you learn below:

Skill #36 –
How to Crochet

You will need a crochet hook and yarn to practice this skill! Start with a large hook and thick yarn if you can.

Start by watching some videos about how to crochet for beginners. Practice each of these skills. Draw lines to match each term to the picture that describes it.

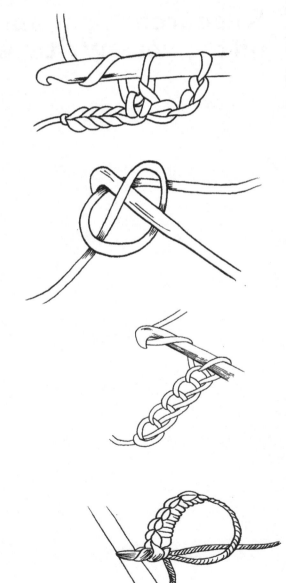

Slip knot

Single crochet

Magic ring

Double crochet

In order to read any crochet pattern, you'll need to learn what the abbreviations mean. Look up what each of these mean, write the definition on the line, and then draw a picture to help you remember what it is!

st – _____

sl st – _____

ch – _____

sc – _____

hdc – _____

dc – _____

tr – _____

dtr – _____

BL – _____

FL – _____

sp – _____

sk – _____

rep – _____

w/ – _____

Crochet a Beanie

Follow these steps to crochet a beanie.

Step 1.	Create a magic ring with 8 st
Step 2.	2 sc in each st around (16 sc) Sl st into your first st to close the row Ch 1 to create next row
Step 3.	Sc into same space as chain 2 sc in next st (1 sc in next st 2 sc in next st) (24 sc) Close row, Ch 1 to create next row
Step 4.	Sc in first st and next st 2 sc in next st (1 sc in next 2 st 2 sc in next st) (32 sc) Close row, Ch 1 to create next row
Step 5.	Sc in first st and next 2 st 2 sc in next st (1 sc in next 3 st 2 sc in next st) (40 sc) Close row, Ch 1 to create next row
Step 6.	Sc in first st and next 3 st 2 sc in next st (1 sc in next 4 st 2 sc in next) (48 sc) Close row, Ch 1 to create next row
Step 7.	Sc in first st and next 4 st 2 sc in next st (1 sc in next 5 st 2 sc in next st) (56 sc) Close row, Ch 1 to create next row

Step 8. Sc in first st and next 5 st
2 sc in next st
1 Sc in next 6 st (64 sc)
Close row, Ch 1 to create next row

Step 9. Sc in first st and next 6 st
2 sc in next st
(1 Sc in next 7 st
   2 sc in next st) (72 sc)
Close row, Ch 1 to create next row

Step 10. Sc in first st and next 7 st
2 sc in next st
(1 Sc in next 8 st
2 sc in next st) (80 sc)
Close row, Ch 1 to create next row

Step 11. Sc in each st around
Close row, Ch 1 to create next row

Step 12. Rep round 11 until desired length

Step 13. To end, sk 1 st, sl st into next st
Fasten off, weave in ends to hide them.

Draw a picture of your
finished hat here!

Made in the USA
Las Vegas, NV
11 August 2023

75971753R00090